Dinosaurs

Diplodocus

Daniel Nunn

www.heinemann.co.uk/library
Visit our website to find out more information about Heinemann Library books.

To order:
Phone 44 (0) 1865 888066
Send a fax to 44 (0) 1865 314091

Visit the Heinemann Bookshop at www.heinemann.co.uk/library to browse our catalogue and order online.

First published in Great Britain by Heinemann Library, Halley Court, Jordan Hill, Oxford OX2 8EJ, part of Harcourt Education. Heinemann is a registered trademark of Harcourt Education Ltd.

Editorial: Daniel Nunn and Rachel Howells
Illustrations: Maureen and Gordon Gray, James Field of Simon Girling and Associates
Design: Joanna Hinton-Malivoire
Picture research: Erica Newbery
Production: Duncan Gilbert

Printed and bound in China by South China Printing Co. Ltd.

10 digit ISBN 0 431 18451 8 (hardback)
13 digit ISBN 978 0431 184517 (hardback)

11 10 09
10 9 8 7 6 5 4 3 2

10 digit ISBN 0 431 18458 5 (paperback)
13 digit ISBN 978 0431 184586 (paperback)

12 11 10 09 08
10 9 8 7 6 5 4 3 2 1

British Library Cataloguing in Publication Data
Nunn, Daniel
Diplodocus. – (Dinosaurs)
567.9'13
A full catalogue record for this book is available from the British Library

Acknowledgements
The publishers would like to thank the following for permission to reproduce photographs: Alamy pp. 21 and 22 (blickwinkel); Corbis pp. 6 (Zefa/ Peter Adams), 7 and 23 (Zefa/Harald Lange), 18 (Ted Soqui), 22 (Craig Lovell); Getty Images pp. 20 and 23 (The Image Bank/Grant Faint); p. 13 Istock/Jurie Maree; Science Photo Library p. 19 (Joyce Photographics).

Cover photograph of Diplodocus reproduced with permission of Corbis/Harald Lange/zefa.

Every effort has been made to contact copyright holders of any material reproduced in this book. Any omissions will be rectified in subsequent printings if notice is given to the publishers.

Contents

The dinosaurs

Dinosaurs were reptiles.

Dinosaurs lived long ago.

Diplodocus was a dinosaur.
Diplodocus lived long ago.

Today there are no Diplodocus.

Some dinosaurs were small.

But Diplodocus was very big.

Diplodocus had a very long tail.

Diplodocus had strong legs.

Diplodocus had a very long neck.

Diplodocus had a small head
and a very small brain.

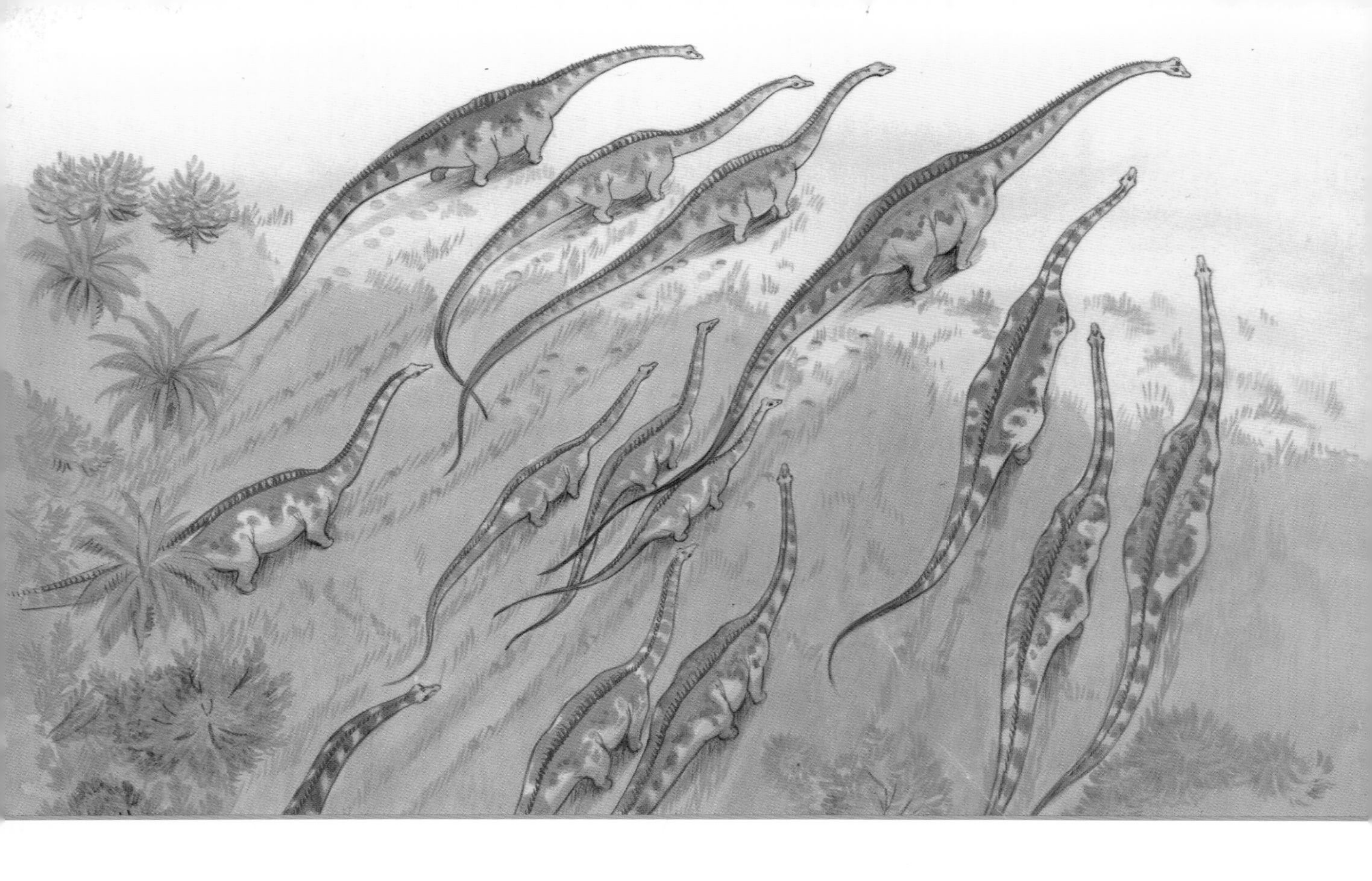

Diplodocus lived in herds. They searched for food together.

Diplodocus ate plants.

Sometimes, other dinosaurs attacked Diplodocus.

Diplodocus used its tail to fight back.

How do we know?

Scientists have found fossils of Diplodocus.

Fossils are the bones of animals which have turned to rock.

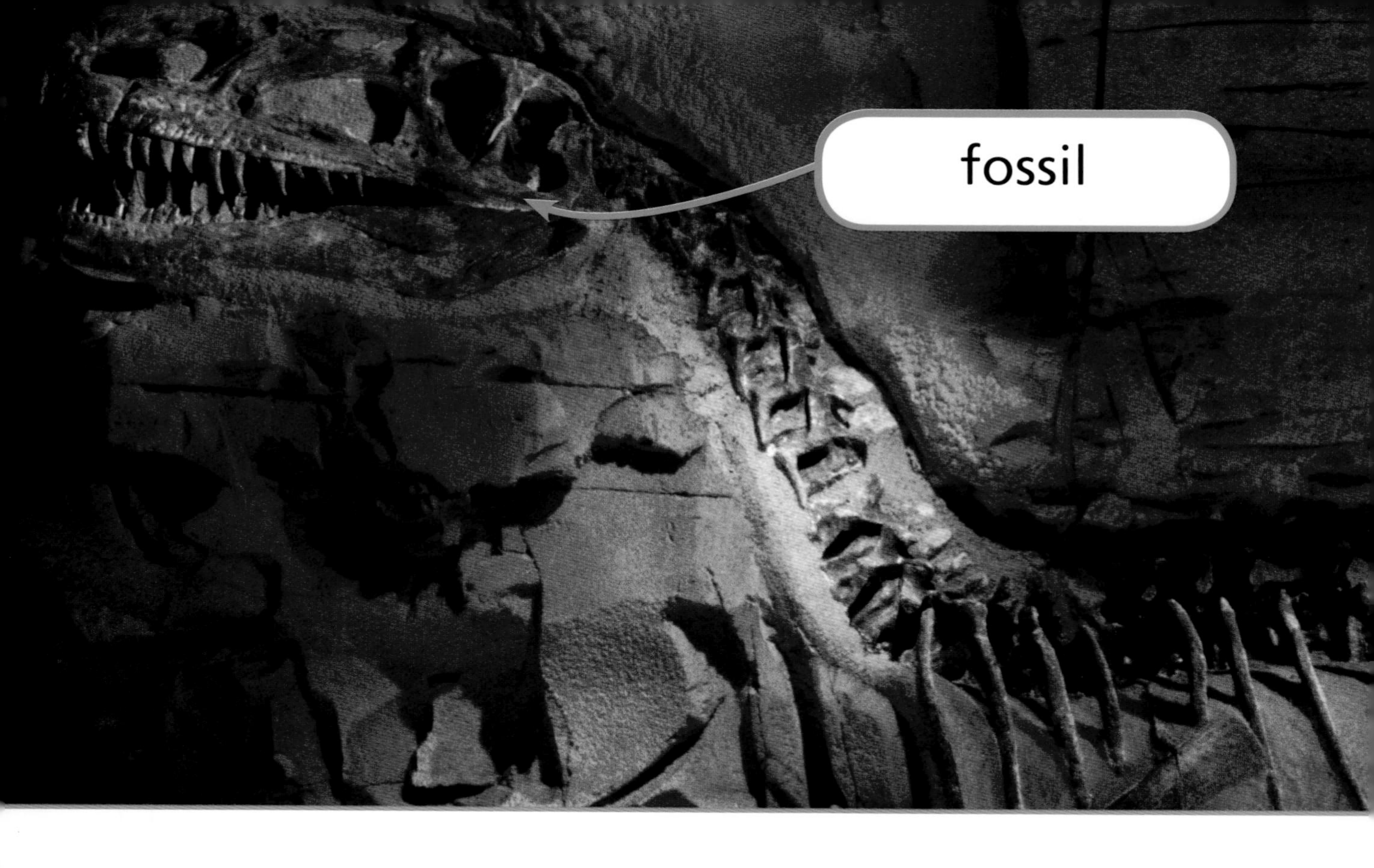

Fossils show us the outline
of the dinosaur.

Fossils tell us what Diplodocus was like.

Fossil quiz

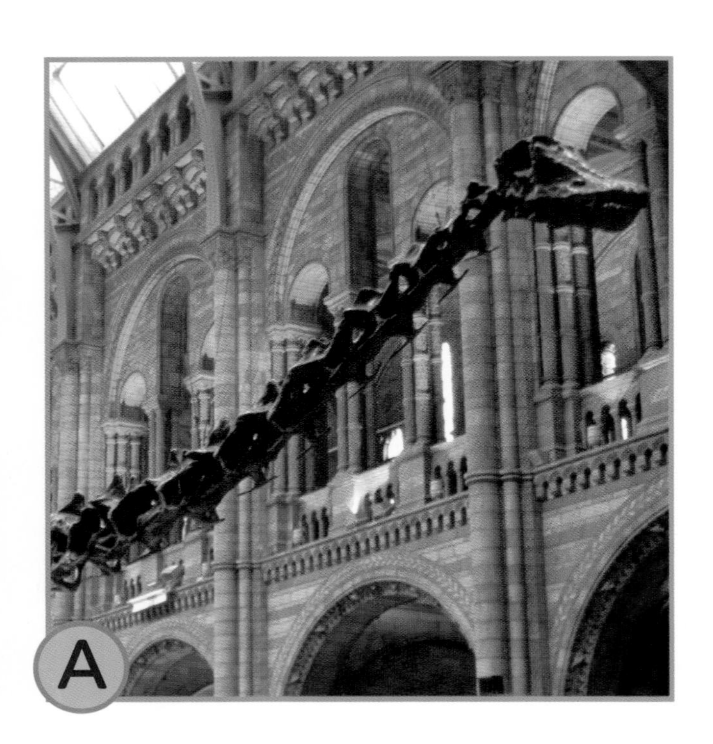

One of these fossils was Diplodocus.
Can you tell which one?

Picture glossary

dinosaur a reptile who lived millions of years ago

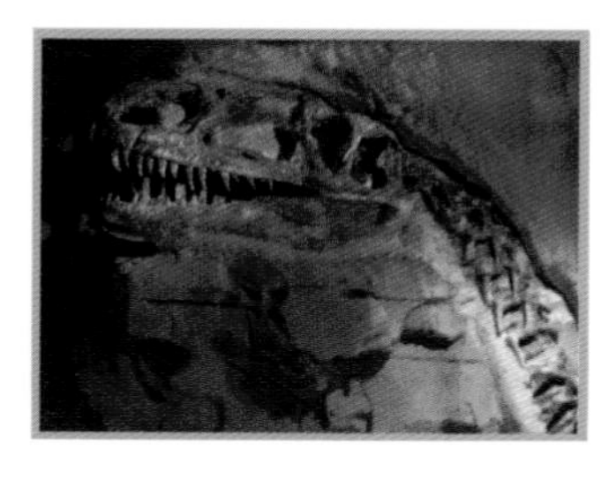

fossil part of a dead plant or animal that has become hard like rock

reptile a cold-blooded animal

Answer to question on page 22

Fossil A was Diplodocus.
Fossil B was Tyrannosaurus rex.

Index

Note to Parents and Teachers
Before reading
Talk to the children about dinosaurs. Do they know the names of any dinosaurs? What features did they have e.g. long neck, bony plates, sharp teeth? Has anyone seen a dinosaur fossil or model in a museum?

After reading
- Make a fossil: Make up a mixture of plaster of Paris, sand and water. Pour into shallow trays. Insert sticks to represent the bones. Allow the mixture to dry. Hide the trays in sand. Give the children brushes and ask them to search for the dinosaur bones.
- Watch the DVD 'Walking with Dinosaurs' (BBC)
- Use percussion instruments to make up a Diplodocus dance e.g. plodding, swaying, swinging tail, reaching up with long neck.

Titles in the *Dinosaurs* series include:

Hardback 978-0431184500

Hardback 978-0431184517

Hardback 978-0431184494

Hardback 978-0431184470

Hardback 978-0431184463

Hardback 978-0431184487

Find out about other titles from Heinemann Library on our website www.heinemann.co.uk/library